LH 0037566 7

KU-995-401

THE WEAVER BIRDS

THE WEAVER BIRDS

BY

IAN SERRAILLIER

LONDON
MACMILLAN & CO. LTD
1944

FOR ANNE

PRINTED IN GREAT BRITAIN
BY R. & R. CLARK, LIMITED, EDINBURGH

AUTHOR'S NOTE

THE narrative poems in this collection are based on fairy tale, legend and folk-lore. *The Weaver Birds*, one of the oldest fairy stories in the world, comes from India. I heard it told over the radio by an Indian princess. According to her version, the weaver bird carried in his ear a cat, a stick and a rope, as well as the ants and river. It seemed to me a bit hard on the poor bird to be so laden, so I left out the cat, the stick and the rope. I think the poem – as well as the weaver – is the lighter for the omission. *The Basilisk* comes from Ancient Greece, the story of *Urashima* from Japan, *The Bishop and the Devil* from the Rhone Valley, Switzerland. The life of St. Simeon is recorded by his disciple, Antonius, the conversion of the dragon belonging to the year 446. *Jack and the Beanstalk* has some familiar fairy tale incidents: the talking musical instrument, the gold-producing animal, the death of a monster. Its origins can be traced back to primitive man's curiosity about earth and heaven – was there a world above the sky and could man reach it? Hence the stories of how man tried and succeeded in climbing to heaven; he regains a lost wife by way of a cloud-capped mountain, captures the sun by way of a magic tree, and slays a monster giant by way of a beanstalk.

Of the miscellaneous poems little need be said. The stories about St. Brendan of the Voyages (died 577) are probably the work of an Irish monk as late as the twelfth century. *The Hen and the Carp* is a translation of a German poem. I had the poem from a Viennese friend who learnt it as a child from her grandmother.

Many of the poems have appeared in recent issues of *English, Modern Reading, Transformation, Life and Letters Today,*

The Poetry Quarterly, *The New English Weekly*, *The Poetry Review*, *Kingdom Come*, and acknowledgment is hereby made to the editors of these journals for the inclusion of these poems in this volume ; also to the Grey Walls Press for permission to include material which appeared in *Three New Poets* (G.W.P., 1942).

I have three other acknowledgments to make : to Guy Boas, E. B. Sturgis and C. V. Mackenzie.

CONTENTS

Narrative Poems

Sonnets

Miscellaneous

Narrative Poems

THE WEAVER BIRDS

I

THIS is the jungle of no land you know;
swings no broad-axe, man dwells not here; in blessed
abode all creatures are fast friends,
tiger and wolf, gazelle and panther, ant
and grizzly bear; and ever and anon
in pleasant weather lion and lamb
romp merrily together.
Down the wilder-gloom
follow that trail of orchids, fiery as
peacock's tail, to yon juniper where
a nest droops from the bough – wedding home
of the weavers. All around the air is
murmurous with wings. Sing Hymen,
hymenaio! today was their wedding.
Ring bells!
From the tunnelled nest peep
two pairs of eyes, rapture in his, in hers
lagoon and argosy of summer skies.
Their wedding gifts had been no trinklements;
each gave to each his heart – what pledge
more loving? True love he sang, John the groom,
from dawn to shut of day, but Jane his bride,
unique among her sex, was voiceless.
With fond fluttering of pride she listened,
eyes wonder-wide, till night-drop,
till (hush) folding of wing and loving-time.
True love he sang more tuneful than the lute,

the pipe, the viol, the flute, the cymbal : his
voice a still pool with seven swans
afloat to minstrelsy and ripple of harp
long echo-echoing, ah long.

Sudden, in green flame a parrot flings
screaming overhead. What terror was that ?
Who tears down the jungle ? Cowed, the weavers
fled to their nest, peered out timorous,
atune. Louder the tear of tree and crash
of felling, till lo down the clearing
a swell company intrudes. ' Mercy, it's
the Emperor ! ' gasped John.

2

With hoof-hoof
of elephants (lash, you tough tuskers, uproot
and raze all-quiet nature !), with pomp and circumstance
he trod down the jungle – he, the Emperor,
lord of realms, most mighty, most puissant, beaming
from howdah down on his hunters and
trappers and foresters and silken dancers
and brass band. Ho, ho ! what train and trapping !
Clash went the cymbals, and triangles
jingle-jangle-jingled in the jungle.

But toward midday they weakened and in silence
sat down to rest under the juniper tree.
' Now, husband,' said Jane, ' sing to the Emperor.
His visit does us honour – here's a chance
to show our gratitude.'
So the weaver sang –
O lyric, melodious enchantment !
Jane : ' How rapt His Highness ! My love, you'd better
try that song again.' Prouder he sang,
but all unwitting saw not the covetous eye,

the grasping hand. 'This is stuff more sober
than my band,' the Emperor was thinking.
'Suppose I took this songster home, how all
would thrill to hear him – his graceful aria,
trip and trill of his note, swell crescendo
and slim diminuendo!' Greedily
he finished, 'Let me grab him!'

And he did.

3

Most admirable Emperor,

You caged the bird and thought to prove
his voice would raise your palace roof.

What tongue is truer than yours? what truth
is wiser than your wisdom tooth?

But you'll be waiting long and long
to hear the weaver's lilting song,
for it was voiceless Jane you took,
not John.

4

Poor John, brideless, alone, forlorn! in
the loveless jungle lonely as the dead,
his eye big as a well with tears, his heart
woeful as the world, his voice –? seven swans
a-drowning on the broken pool, no harp,
no minstrelsy. Sang he no more.

Then despair
quick as a crocodile snapped jaw
and swallowed him. Blind, round and round
in that rumble-tortured belly he floundered.
'Cheer up!' piped the lamb.

'Courage, husband!'
roared the lion.

'Go seek her, bring her back!' advised
the panther.

'Bring her back, bring her back!'
the jungle echoed.

And the weaver heard.
Hope sparkled in his eye. *Cheer up, go seek her!*
bring her back, his bride! Suddenly,
'I go!' he cried.

5

So he shut up house and farewell flew
far over the jungle, a day and a night
and a day till his pinions ached. Wing-weary,
skimming down through the trees he lighted
where a funeral was passing, a long trail
of mourners winding – 'Ailinon!' they wailed,
'ailinon, ailinon!'

In wonder
he watched, full a thousand corpses
counting in a minute – they were ANTS.
A pall-bearer shouted, 'Where are you going?'
'To the Emperor.'

'What, *him?*'

They halted.
Ant to ant the word passed, 'He's going to
the Emperor.' They buzzed, broke line,
surged round him crying, 'Kill him! revenge!
murder!'

In panic the weaver shouted, 'Friends,
are you mad? What wrong have I done?'

'Not you,'
said a mourner, 'the Emperor's our man.'
Another, 'The Emperor! Put him to the sword!' and
another, 'It's the blood of his elephants
we want. *They* razed our cities, trampled us
to death——'

'– O take us with you,' with one voice
they implored.
'Climb into my ear,'
said the weaver, 'left ear!'
In they poured.
And the dead were left to bury their dead.

6

And after much journeying he reached
Pompopo, a mighty important river, and
lighted on the brink for a drink. While he sipped,
from the watery deep basso profundo
Pompopo spoke: 'Little one – ahem – may I
entreat a word? Where are you going?'
'To
the Emperor.'
'So! I had heard
a rumour of your grievance. I too nurse
– ahem – a grievance,' he grumbled. 'When
the imperial caravanserai without passport
hoity-toity trespassed on my billowy sea,
the Emperor – despise him! – SPAT in me.
Brooding some vengeance, I saw you coming.
At once it occurred to me – maybe
the idea's absurd – if you had cabin room
– ahem – I might——'
'Climb into my ear, right ear,'
said the weaver bird.
'A capital notion,'
said the brother of Ocean. And straightway
that tremendous billowy 'tween-rock-rolling river
wormed from his furrow into the weaver's ear,
packed in snug, all of him. There was just room.
And they set forth.

7

Ah, weaver, does your heart
swoon for your bride ? How fares she, well or ailing,
dead or alive ? With troubled heart and aching
head (so weary weight), struggler, toil on !

From one moon to the next he journeyed,

8

at last to the Palace. This is it, on fair
lawn, city of sparkling tower and minaret
asplash from pots of gold, most glorious.
'Twas built of old, some say from fragments of
the sun.

The Emperor answered the door. 'Your wife ?
'Od's-me-life, I'd quite forgotten her.
Flunkey, where's the prisoner ?' (Prisoner ?
The weaver quaked at the dungeon word.)
'I hope she's still alive. I daresay
you've travelled some way ?'

And he led him to
the Elephant House, dingy and dim,
muck-odorous of beast. O cruelty and filth !
How the weaver's heart boiled with loathing
for this man !

'Here she is,' he announced,
and pointed to a cage tacked to the drinking
trough, wet with hose and fountain, dripping, rotten,
rusty (and locked). 'This is the price of trickery,'
he mocked.

Alas, poor Jane ! Was that sodden
mass of feathers his bride ? She limped to the bars
so painfully he ached for her – 'Dear love !'
she cried.

Then anguish tore him quite. Bitterly
he flew at the cage, beat at the bars,
pecked at the lock in vain, fluttered around
again ; then lighted, hopeless, on the ledge.
'Courage, my love,' he whispered. 'Never tire!
Sure, I'll find some way to set you free.'

But the Emperor laughed, 'We'll see!', unlocked the door
and flung the weaver in. 'That'll be two
for tea,' he chuckled, and fastened the lock. 'Bye-bye!'

So, into the spider's parlour stepped the fly.

9

In that noisome cage hour after hour they lay,
despairing, numb at heart, yet some comfort
to each other ; while outside, in unconcern,
reclining royally in straw the venerable
million-wrinkled elephants winked sleepily.
What bliss their ignorance – already the ants
had smelt their foe and, busy in the weaver's ear,
were marshalling battalions. 'Shed no tear,'
they said. 'Joy cometh in the morning.'
And out of his head like wisdom from her fount
they poured.
At midnight the Emperor woke. Death
of the world, what noise was this ? what monstrous
elephant uproar ? Downstairs, over
the dark lawn (candle and pyjamas) he
hurried to the House, opened the windy door. . . .
The candle flickered. . . . And silence struck him,
ghastly, no breath, no snore. . . . There in the moonlight
lay his elephants, sprawled in heaps of late
agony – the ants had stung 'em to death,
one and all.

'Tomorrow, execution ! Off
with your heads ! ' said the Emperor. ' Till then I take
no risks. Tonight you sleep by my bed.'

'Twas a four-poster and from the cross-beam
the weavers' cage – with cock and hen – swung
a-tremble to the Emperor's snores. ' O
misery ! ' cried Jane, ' to lie for ever
helpless in this prison, no friend to save us
from distress ! '

A deep voice yawned, ' No friend ? '
' Who's that ? '

' Did I hear an S.O.S. ? '
And with much splashing Pompopo, sleepy-head,
hauled himself from river-bed and, parting
the bulrushes, peeped from the weaver's ear :
' I'm yours, sir, to obey.'

' See the Emperor
below ? ' said John. ' He turns in his sleep. Quick,
before he wakes, wash him away !——'

' – but don't
drown us,' said Jane.

' Whatever you say.'
Straightway the river poured from the weaver's ear,
from that tiny source tremendous, till the floor
was swimming and the swell of the tide lifted
the bed as Noah's Ark from Ararat :
forth terrific with blood afire onrushing
smashed the gilt windows and ground 'em down
in boiling foam. On swept the Emperor,
astride his thunder-bed or under, dodging
unsoberly Scylla the minaret, Charybdis
the pagoda – bump, breathless over a waterfall ;
while overhead top-heavy peacocks
lurched off screaming in terror. How jogged

he was and jostled, his bleeding shoulders
scraped to the bone. And Agg the Sea-cat clawed
him, Leviathan the whale sucked in
his watery breath and spouting it in geysers
swamped him. Stout was the storm, the four-poster
over the pinnacle waves hopped high ; yet ever
the weavers' cage like masthead lantern
lightly rocked above, clear of all pother.
And the Emperor ? O wild eyes and frothing lips !
O mouth spitting oath and mackerel ! while
the birds exultant were singing :

May gout cramp his little toe,
smelly fish kiss him,
and nothing that is stickiest
or slimiest miss him !

Ugsome frogs, plop down his throat
to chill his boiling belly,
and strings of loathly spawn muff
his neck in clammy jelly !

'Enough !' gasped the Emperor. 'By Satan's beard,
I can stand it no more !'
'You give in ?'
'Weaver,
dictate your terms.'
'First, that we be freed ; second
that you be spared.'
'Agreed !' He tottered upright,
reached for the cage, unlocked.
'Onaway !'
the weaver cried. 'Gay lover, upride in joy !'
And she with tender bill-and-cooing replied,
'Lo, sweeting, I come !'

Aerial they rose
— O gala day ! — together from shipwreck
soared to the grinning sun.
And it came to pass
that the waters abated and the imperial
four-poster touched dry land.

II

Conclusion now.
You ask, what of the river, Pompopo ?
The Emperor (reformed) dubbed him imperial
and bound him for ever and a day
to lap his realms. How proud he is, for now
down him rides gloriously that great whale
Leviathan, a top-notcher, with seven
hundred knuckles in his spine.

And the ants?
By magic prefix they were changed from ants
to eleph-ants and willing dwell at the palace
with no loss of wisdom, serenely wise.

And last, the weavers. Measure not in word
their blessing for it brims as the ocean,
no tongue can tell it. Their heart would not squander
in show nor waste in royal finery,
but fleet with twang of arrow homeward
went winging. 'Blow, wind! lift us, weather!
Far kith and kin, drape the nest for our coming!'
Heart to heart, wing to wing they flew
home to joy of long loving, to seven swans
afloat and sweeping harp. Ah paradise,
dear jungle! Over the tree-tops, over
the tiny-rippled river, beyond the mountains and
the wilderness they flew with feather o' yearning,
homebound, ah homebound.

JACK AND THE BEANSTALK

I

HE climbed and climbed. Swinging, tugging,
he hauled aloft as sailor into rigging.
Who was he, this lad so squirrel-nimble?
Could he be Jack, the limb-slop lazy,
Jack holy mad, plumb crazy? O he climbed with a will,
sure-footed, hand over hand. Swinging, tugging,
he hauled aloft as sailor into rigging.
To dout his dizziness, 'I'm scared o' nowt,'
he said. Haul away, heave-ho!
Deep below was the whaleback down, sheep
tiny as flies, far off to sea ships
like floating seeds; and Earth a chessboard
in harvest gold and green with royal clouds
to play. See them, King and Queen,
strut martially from field to field, while he,
common Jack, hauled to kingdom come.
Good to be quit of home. Good
to be venturous – but what of mum?

Crazy Jack, mazy Jack,
devil-may-care so lazy Jack!

Sure, she had the gift of the gab for werriting,
her main delight to rasp and nag at him
from morn to night. 'Get up, slugabed!
clean the fowl, polish my boots, put out the cat,
fetch this, fetch that!' O
'twas parlous good to be quit of mum –
she was ever fiery or grim glum
and would no sooner smile than beetle swallow a bun.

As he hauled aloft, slowly the sun
slid down heaven, beyond the purple clouds,
dropped yonder – a red coin into his slot of sea.

'Twas bone-windy, boisterous cold, the air
so nimble the lad rose light as gossamer,
wondering, ' How soon
do I leave this stalk amazing for the moon ? '
And he scanned below, saw but a vapour swimming,
no land : above – one last leaf and brimming
night.
                    On that leaf he lay, fagged o' limb,
close wrapt in the palm of it ; yawned, shut eye,
for dark had fallen and he was slumberfull.

2

At sun-up he woke and from the top leaf leapt
to land, to a fair countree of flower, hill
and sunny cloud. Coiled on a stone an adder cried,
' Morning, stranger ! I'm here to meet you, greet you,
cry you welcome.'
                                    ' Take heed ! ' warned a woodpecker.
' A word from the wisebird to a wisdomlack –
turn back ! d'you mark me, turn——' but headlong, heed-
    less Jack
was away and away. O this was heaven ! . . .
                                                            But was it ?
Meandering down tangled lanes
and silent woodland ways, sudden he heard
a thunderclap roll overland. Forked lightning
struck. And the ground was scorched black, as it were
dragon-blasted. Between black hills valleys
gaped like wounds. Ah desolation !
No wing but carrion crow,
no flower but blood-red berry, Bitter-sweet,
no tree but gloomy hemlock that grew foul fungus,
dead men's fingers. And far off, against the storm,
against the thunder-cloud rose Blackest Castle.
Hic, hoc the carrion crow ! roll, thunder !

drench, rain ! bleed red, cruel berry !
Ugh.
Toward the castle he pressed, for shelter.

3

From the window a voice was singing
sadly :

' While I am prisoned in dungeon walls
(nor swallow dips nor lavrock calls),
a blank my heaven
hung with snow,
yet never the wonder falls.

' O find me, lover ! raise me where
our storm-forsaken heaven's aflare
with saffron, and
pine scent and hawthorn
melt in sweet air.'

All which was double dutch to Jack. Drenched
he was, homeless in a weird countree.
' O shelter me, singer, whoever you are,
shelter me ! '
The window flew open wide,
out stared a lady's head, two fear-full eyes
where hope blazed awhile and died.
' Lad, you startled me,' she cried. ' I thought
you might be – never mind ! ' and sighed.
' Hast a bite of food, gudwife ? '
' Meat in plenty.'
' A dry shirt ? '
' Big enough for four and twenty.'
' And board and bed ? '
' Aye, lad, the vaults are empty.
Lie there in royal state, and Death
shall be thy bedmate.'

'I'll challenge him. You'll see,
gudwife, which is the better of we.'
'Foolish boy, this is no house of innocence.
Dungeon walls have savage faces,
Murther down in clanking places
makes wild music of screw and socket-wrenching rack.'
'I'm scared o' nowt,' said Jack.
She smiled bitterly. 'Dinna say
I havna warned ye,' and opened the door
to let him in.

4

And while he ate she told him of Macgregor
the giant, 'So huge, yon strip of sky, lad,
that's his bed, and yon grim cloud
the pillow for his head. . . . Ten years ago
he stole me for his bride. Unlovely as a crutch
and twice as wooden (for him that's saying much),
how could I love him ? Ever he thralls me, beats me,
calls me never sweeting but shunface, drudge.'
'Gudwife, I'll slay him.'
'You so wee
to trounce the high and mighty ? Wait
till he comes. One smite of his club'll prove
your fancy flighty. Dead, he'll grind your bones
to make his bread, scrape your sweat for butter
and fry your flesh for apple fritter. . . . Whisht !
I hear him now. Head over into the oven with 'ee !
Quick, lad, hide ! '
From the oven, dungeon-dark,
he heard the door grind open
(bolts and shackles, how it squeaked and rattled !),
saw through the crack, tremendous on the stone,
the giant. An ambling alp he was, with whiskered
top. 'Ho, mealy-mouth, my dinner, what ? '
Then all at once his eyes shot out, teeth

flashed terrible, a tombstone grin :

' Fee fi fo fum
I smell the blood of an Englishman.
Be he alive or be he dead
I'll grind his bones to make my bread.'

' They're ground already, love,' the gudwife said.
' It's young blood I smell.'
' The gravy to the joint,
dear chick. I've basted well.'
' Be it savoury,'
he grunts, ' I'm satisfied. Now first
my rump of beef and dozen of wine.'
He tucks
his bull-hide napkin in his shirt, sticks in
with trident fork. Such greed he shows and thirst
you'd say his belly-barn must surely burst.
Anon he calls for harp and hen – a golden
egg, a tune !
Ah, magic harp, by no finger-touch
sweet music sweeps over your strings, drowsy,
melodious, on charmèd wings of sleep.
Ah, wondrous hen, that each bar can bring
a golden egg. Macgregor lies, rests,
digests.
Soon music, wine and wassail
riot in his brain. He droops, sleeps
soundly . . . snore . . . snore. . . .
If he should wake no more !

5

' Goodbye, Macgregor,
it's time that I was leaving.
Sleep sound while you may,
for next time we're meeting

blood will flow in bucketfuls –
    yours I'm meaning
(when David met Goliath, lay
    Goliath's head bleeding).
How swoons the harp, how temptingly
    the golden eggs are gleaming!
" Master, will you miss us much
    when he's been thieving?" –
Bye-bye, bully huff,
    I'm leaving.'

6

Snore . . . snore. . . .
Asleep for evermore?
                    'Out of the oven
with 'ee, Jack!'
                'One day, gudwife, I'm coming back,
for half I wish that you was mother to me.'
Tiptoe he crept toward the table. 'Now
to take——'
'Thief!' cackled the hen and quaked. The harp
cried, 'Master, wake!'
                    Both she grabbed and clapped 'em
to his side. 'Hold on to 'em like mad. . . . The wine
is spent, he's stirring, lad . . . away with you!'
Away he went.
                The bleary giant, reeling to his feet,
saw fast vanishing his live two-legged meat.
'Wet smack of a bumboy! I'll catch you,'
he bawled.
            But she flipped him and tripped him
so he tumbled heavily: stumbled
up and out.
            The gudwife from the window

was straining after Jack, anxious, with a mother's eye.
' God keep you, lad – His blessing ! Run, O run ! '

So fast he ran his slippers struck the sun.

7

And the clumsy giant sped after him.
Fient a boddle, how he cursed, how
he threatened and thumped ! and did he gad the hoof !
Over hill and broken dale they whipped away
a night and a day, by field and drumly stream,
through moor and moss and many a mire, away
and away. And the cunning adder hissed
from his stone, ' No need to hurry. Do please stay.'
And the woodpecker : ' Hey, windylegs,
journeyman Jack, heed the word of a wisebird
to a wisdomlack –

If ever you get to Ladder o' Bean,
dangle, drop under cover of green,
and *don't* come back ! '

8

At last, at the foot of that huge beanstalk
he touched ground and, craning upward, saw the giant
hurtling down on him. Swift
an axe he found and chopped and chopped till the stalk
was hewn. It tottered breathlessly, sagged, flung
Macgregor clear. One moment his shadow sprawled
across the sun ; the next, down the screaming air
he roared, this moon mountain, this whirling thunder.
Crash-landed. A forest crumpled under him
like grass. Full length he lay along two acres spread,
groaned horrible, rolled over, dead.

' And now,' said Jack, ' off with his head.'

9

On the steps of the tumbledown his mother (you
remember her ? ponderous and girthy,
her soul much of the earth, earthy)
greeted him in vinegar : ' What's this mess ? '
and blitzed him roundly. But when
the hen began to lay and harp
to discourse sweet music, ' Curse ' became ' Bless
you, smart lad ! how wrong to call you dunce ! '
And she snaffled hen and harp and locked 'em up at once.
So greedy. So vulgar. So tough.

And now the harp's a business (his mother's doing),
hired out for *soirées musicales*.
What with that and a golden egg a day
you'd call the money prospect good, for J
can live as a prince now if he would.
But mum's the squanderer, lives like a queen,
frocked in ermine, silk, or crêpe de chine.

Laugh at her there in coach and four
(diamond panes, and gilt initials on
the door), pranked up in jewelled swank and gallimumfery galore . . .
                    while Jack slinks off alone
and minds the gudwife, his promise to climb to her.
Yon wood of scarlet runners, that's his sowing.
As hour by hour he sits to watch 'em growing,
' O for a Ladder o' Bean,' he sighs, ' and I'll
be up and going. How long, how long ? waiting's weary
and life on earth unutterably dreary.'
Sometimes, searching heaven for sign of her
he sees a light cloud (pillow for Macgregor's head),
a blue strip of sky (his empty bed) ;
beyond – thunder and blackest walls,
and beyond again – who knows what loneliness
in lonely halls ?
                    And away he wanders, head
in cloud, moodily, for ever dreaming and remembering
' that fair gudwife, far away
in a weird countree '.

Call it, if you will, a happy ending.

THE BALLAD OF ST. SIMEON

LISTENER, this is the tale of Simeon, blessed Saint,
who by God's grace
sat on a pole and ran the straight race.

' O Lord, I'm sick of this city, all
its gallimumfery and trumpery,
ungodliness and devil-toasting,
emptiness and hollow-boasting –
what true man can love it ? '
Not that he thought himself above it,
but his ways were lonely and he loved God.
So he decided for the good of his soul
to ' move closer to God and live on a pole '.

He bought a forty-foot timber,
hammer and nails, a round platform
big enough to sit on or slumber ;
chose a site, acting on his mother's advice,
and planted the pole in the ground. And Azzah his mother
painted it and made it look nice.
With a rucksack on his back
he mounted. ' Ha, ha ! ' the people hooted,
' the martyr mounts to the rack ! '
As the pole shivered to his weight
the nimble scooted round and shouted,
' See he totters now, our heaven-aspiring
steeple-jack ! '

The blowy wind twiddled up to him much dust
and nasty murmurs – the Elders :
' This grisly Noah rides the flood and leaves
us, drowning rats,
to watch him perch on Ararat.'
Then Azzah his mother, ' No indeed ' (she grieves

for their malice), ' as long as he floats
he'll keep his life-boats
handy for your need.'
The Elders mocked her. ' You wish him a saint ?
perhaps a martyr ? – we'd like to see him bleed.'
And scorning Simeon on his solitary station
they labelled him unfit for canonisation,
while the common people, though their words were quaint,
meant much the same when they said, ' He ain't no saint.'
And the last voice the wind sent was this :
' By the might of Ammon,
he can't deny he's scared stiff of the dragon.'

Now there lived in a warm cave near that place
a fiery dragon, and all knew
it was because of him that no grass grew.
Man-pie was his lick-lip delight,
and the population of that city varied according
to the bite of his appetite.
With deep regret Simeon would watch
that dragon in foam of black foul fumes smoking
down the city corridors, smacking
up morsels – children in rompers,
mothers in jumpers, Elders and ex-Mayors
busy at corners with Pharisee prayers.
A few resisted, in fire-proof Shadrach suits,
but they weren't much use.
Verily since Ammon
nobody had quelled a dragon.
And Simeon prayed God give him grace
to rebuke that dragon or dout it.
For the present he felt he could do nothing about it.

Years Simeon stood, sat, slept
on his pole, communed with God and wept
for the sin-smudged city. Some, not many,

brought him their troubles and he offered
prayers for them but could do no miracle.
And he suffered.
The seasons steam-rollered him. In summer
the flaming sun made him boil

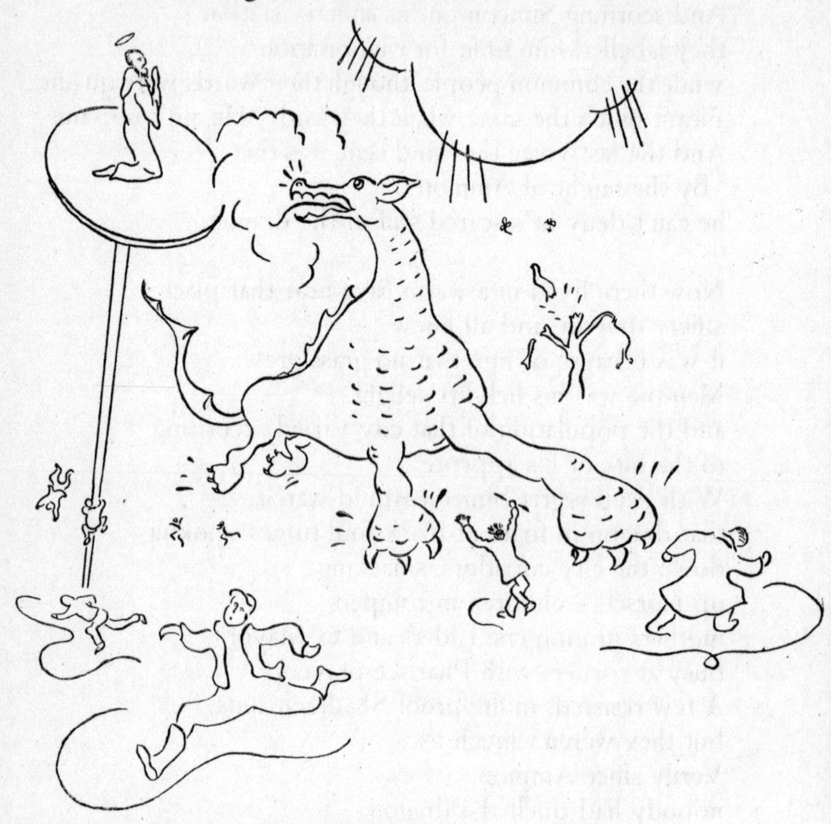

and the pole paint bubble and pop, and
when winter was a turmoil
of flying icicles, in spite of his mother-knitted clothes,
his goose skin hugged his skeleton. So cold was it
that chilblains marbled and the people's oaths
froze on the air (thawing out in Spring
with a bang).

And always in all weathers his view
was the same – on grassless mud
the graceless nickelodeons of the rich and
across the cobbled avenue
the unfumigated shacks of the poor.
And many times
to dulcimer and tabor and all kinds of sweet music men flocked
to Church for the marrying and Mound for the burying. But
lots
because of the dragon, the man-eater, died in their socks;
they lie in his belly now, wide as a whale's,
under living tombstones of bristling scales.

As an oddity the solemn Simeon was eminent.
'See him on his high horse', 'Simeon's Agony Column', these
posters were everywhere so prominent
that tourists rolled up from afar for a visit
('So that's him, is it?'). And under the pole
Azzah his mother harangued them proudly:
'He'd never have stuck it
without the wholesome meals I send him
daily by pulley, rope and bucket.'

Jump now to the last day of the last month
of the fortieth year, the world
just finishing its sun-round roll,
that patient man (his seat sore-vexed with sitting)
still up the pole,
and his mother on the ground quietly knitting.
Dim on the skyline suddenly he saw a dusty pother
of cloud. 'What is it, mother? the dragon?'
'Yea verily a snorter,
coughing up venom and breathing out slaughter.'
She hopped. 'See, in somersaults he comes and catherine-
wheels,'
and cumberly she took to her antique heels.

And the dragon came.
And his hoarse hissings, thick breath and hobbled gait
proved that mothers can exaggerate.
Strange, thought Simeon, that pain-full tear
in place of the usual knock-me-down cheer.
' Now, my son, what's wrong ? ' he asked,
' Are you sick and dying ? '
But it was long before the dragon could speak for crying.
' My eye,' he sobbed, ' my poor right eye.'
Simeon peered. ' I'm a bit short-sighted,' –
peered closer. ' It looks to me to have sprouted.'
And the dragon sobbed, ' Oh misery me,
can't you see it's bunged up with a tree ? '
Then, humbly, he bowed himself to a wheel.
' Please, man of God,' he said, ' heal
me of my grievous wound and bless——'
' I'll do my best,' said Simeon, ' but first you must confess.'
The dragon sighed.
' Must I ? it's so undignified.'
Then with piteous tear smothering his pride he began :
' I think . . . I once . . . ate a man——'
He groaned. ' Lean Joseph was first, –
When I'd gobbled his brother, Tim Buck, too
I confined my meals to the well-to-do :
Helenus, Diana (the Mayor's daughter) – .
I ironed her out in the Latin quarter ;
Next Dives, Midas, and . . .' That was the gist,
and the Big Sun travelled as he reeled off the list.
Not a word did Simeon hear,
for he was busy, locked with the Lord in prayer.
At last, confession done,
the blessed Simeon, brimming with Power,
looked down, and straightway
the tree jumped out of the dragon's eye.
Then that dire dragon, uncumbered of his load,
whooped with joy. And Simeon said,

when he'd got over his surprise,
'Truly in God
is every brute beast wise
and every savage creature gentle.'

And the people,
peeping mouse-timid from cottage and croft,
from hole in lattice or window crannie
or missing slate in a loft,
veritably wondered. What miracle was this? –
the dragon, recently a riot
now coiled meekly, utterly quiet?
And as they watched spell-bound,
a word from the Man of Miracles unwound
him from his coils, rolled
his long length on the ground,
then packed him off to Church,
where worthily for just on two hours he worshipped.

On his exit he tripped
a gay measure, up-street and down dancing
and whistling a ditty: till Simeon called him,
'Ho, dragon!' and asked,
'What d'you think of our city?'
He stopped in his step to consider, then zipped
right round the wall and returned in a jiffy.
'A pity,' he said, 'but methinks' (with a sniffy)
'it stinks.'
Then Simeon cheered. 'That's just as I feared.
Now by the might of St. Ammon
I give you the power to destroy and renew it.'
'O master,' said the dragon, 'I'll willingly do it.'
While the people flew out of their homes
he pulled out his furnace damper and stoked
up the fire. And his nostrils bellowed and smoked
and he vomited crackling tongues of flame
that lashed out ever stronger and stronger

till presto ! their city was no longer.
Then, as Orpheus with his music made
Thebes, so the dragon by whistling a ditty
conjured up bricks, tiles and mortar
from every quarter,
raising a royal new city.
And the people marvelled at this vision
of domes, merry mansions, cupolas,
flats with balconies, pewter pagodas,
marquees of blue millinery with golden masts
and green neighbourhood of meadow-grass !
This first of miracles did Simeon.
And the people praised him and hallelujah hailed him
Saint, raining him as he slid down the pole
with confetti and cheers.
Can you wonder if
while he walked he wobbled all funny ? After forty years
his cramped stumps were stiff.

Then the Elders spoke with one voice :
' Come to our pavilions,
all of you, salaried and poor, masters and minions.
Rejoice, for we shall hold a Feast
in glory of Simeon and this gentle Beast.'

So, led by the dragon, the people
huge in procession entered that city dancing
to dulcimer and tabor and all kinds of sweet music,
Simeon and his mother following.

And after, when all was over, Azzah his mother
in her venerable antiquity,
her legs rickety, her nerves a bit crotchety,
gathered in her two sons, Simeon and (by adoption)
the dear dragon. And leaving that city
they went to the dragon's fire-cave and lived there, three
in serenity.

THE THREE BEARS

1

DEEP in the mazy wood entwined, a cottage!
'I wonder who lives here,' said Goldilocks.
'How beautiful!' The summer hedge is strung
with beads and cobwebs dewy as her shoes.
She pauses wander-weary, peeps
beyond at the sleepy garden, round-yawning:
daisy blinks, poppy still sleeps,
over the porch the dew-wild eyes
of the dog-rose flash in scorn
down at the dandelion, tousled stranger on the lawn –
O brush your ragged hair, dandelion!
'I *do* wonder who lives here.'
Under the oak tree paddle in silent pool
the yellow irises; between their toes, look,
goldfish wink and play at hide-and-seek.
Now the garden wakes, sea-pink and hollyhock,
frogcup and lily, the fair first bloom
of morning. Unseen the cricket plucks
his fiddle strings; along the path the blue
bombardier beetle hustles. 'I'll follow too,'
said Goldilocks.
She moves the wicket, runs up the path,
tiptoe reaches for the knocker, knocks
one, two, three! . . . No answer?
One . . . two . . . the door creaks ajar.
'Anyone at home?'
Hiss-ss-ss.
Strange –
Hello, a kettle hissing on the range!

2

A white scrubbed table, three bowls
of porridge, one big, one medium, one small,

and on the wall
a longlegs and a dumbledore. What more surprises?
Three plush chairs (same quality, three sizes)
and over the mantelshelf a Mayor's
portrait inscribed in gilt lettering
YOURS TRULY GRANFER BEAR.
'Oh dear,
what a funny picture! Who *can* live here?'
'You'll soon see,'
hissed the kettle hazily.

She tried the big plush chair, ROCK, O much
too hard: then the middle plush chair, FEATHER, much
too soft: last the little one – delight!
just right.

'Poof, porridge!' cried the cloudy kettle,
and the lid began a patter dance.
'I'm so hungry,' said Goldilocks. 'There's nobody about....
What a chance——'
'to try me,'
said the porridge invitingly. 'What a chance
to try me!'
'Just one bite. Would it matter?'
And the porridge steamed, 'You'll soon see.'

She tried the big bowl, much too piping hot:
the middle bowl, much too clammy cold:
last the little one – delight!
just right, and gobbled up the lot.

3

Meanwhile three bears, who had left their porridge cooling,
down the deep wood with roll and rocking gait
were strolling, strolling:

Father Bear, with grisly teeth and gruesome twinkle ;
Mother Bear, brunette with scarce a wrinkle
and sentimental snout all love and nozzle ;
and smallest – snapping snail, chasing hare,
skipping over the purl-and-babble brook and everywhere –
their hearty youngster, Baby Bear.
Past the Oaks, Old Men in jacket o' leaf and mossy trousers,
past pock-holed beeches with vast armpits,
among the wild mulberries and larches, the tangle
of woodbriar, creeper twirled
in bough and bramble – in this their wide world
merrily they ambled.
And in the tree-tops the birds were trilling
while, a glade away, grimly sounded :
chip-chop ! chip-chop !
' What's that, daddy ? '
' Our foe the woodcutter. He's axeing early.
They say he has a pretty daughter named——'
' Good day, good day ! ' piped a blackbird
pert and sprightly.
' Mornin', family ! ' kraaked a crested jay
equally politely.
Past the waterfall
they strolled, through the Great Clearing.
' We must be homing, homing, for I hear
the kettle humming,' said Mother Bear.
So off they hurried, away through the birchwood,
down the chestnut avenue (' Breakfast,
breakfast ! ' the birds began to shout)
till the cottage came in sight.
' Here we are at last,' sighed Little Bear
and nosed the wicket open. ' I *am* hungry.'
Pa
stopped dead. His voice was thunder : ' Ma,
did *you* leave the front door ajar ? '

4

Tiptoe into the parlour.
Sniff.
'Who's there?'
'We are,' said kettle, porridge bowls and table;
'We are,' said longlegs and dumbledore.
They glanced at the chairs (where
Father and Mother loved to snore together
while Little Bear tickled their noses with a feather).

'Who's been sitting in my chair?' growled Big Bear.
'Who's been sitting in my chair?' grumbled Mother Bear.
'Who SAT in my chair?' wailed Little Bear.
'Wouldn't you like to know?' said
the kettle. How the lid shook
with laughter and the red coals hissed
and hissed! But look –

'Who's been messing with my porridge?' growled Big Bear.
'Who's been messing with my porridge?' grumbled Mother
Bear.
'Who's gobbled up all *my* porridge?' sobbed Little Bear.
Mother peered through her spectacles. 'My poor, poor dear,'
but already the bowl was a-swim with tears.

'I see trouble brewing,' stormed Big Bruin,
his brow cloudy as the kettle, his face
grim and grisly,
his temper like a hairbrush bristly.
'Clearly,' thought Mother, 'I must stand on my mettle.'
'Stand on your mettle!'
echoed the kettle,
and the red coals hissed. 'Overflowing everywhere,
bother it! I'll make the tea at once,' said Mother Bear.
'No!' scowled Father. 'We search the house
before we settle.'
'Try upstairs,' said the kettle.

5

' Goldilocks ! ' a voice was calling through
the greenwood. ' Goldilocks, where are you ? '
Anxiously among the mulberries the woodcutter
searched, among the beeches and Old Men Oaks.
' Goldilocks ! Goldilocks ! '
Down the worried avenues he ran
while the woods took their fill
of first sun.
' Tell me, blackbird with the yellow bill,
have you seen my little one ? '
' Good day, good day ! '
was all the blackbird could say.
' Ho there, sentinel ! You, crested jay !
Has anyone this morning passed this way ? '
And the crested jay replied unsmiling,
' I saw three bears come prowling, prowling.'
The woodcutter stiffened. His face went white.
' Pray God I'm not too late ! '
With racing pulse away he ran, past the waterfall,
through the Great Clearing to the birchwood,
down the chestnut avenue, while
in his heart a song moved mournfully :

' Sad, O sad when the sparrow set eye
on the shimmering wings of the dragonfly.
He snapped his beak as she flew by
and that was the death of the dragonfly.'

6

Hush ! tiptoe upstairs
they trod – Father, Mother, Baby Bear.
' Who'll open the bedroom door ? '
' I dare,'
husky-whispered Father, breathed
it open.

Hush.

Tick-tock, tick-tock,

said the bedroom clock. Tick-tock, as the sun streamed
through the window, tick-tock as in gay light they gleamed –
three brass beds with knobs on.

'Who's been sleeping in my bed?' thundered Big Bear
(the counterpane was wrinkled).
'Who's been sleeping in my bed?' rumbled Mother Bear
(the sheet was creased, the bolster crinkled).
'*Who's that sleeping in my bed?*' screamed Little Bear,
his green eyes glowing like fireworks.
'O my whiskers, a human girl!'

There

on the bed, frail as summer flower
Goldilocks lay sleeping, lullay lulla
Goldilocks lay dreaming, on the pillow
spilling her golden hair.

Little Bear clutched the bed rail, shook it till
it rattled like a milk-cart. 'Stand back,
Father! She's my game!'
Up sprang Goldilocks and screamed. With fierce delight
he grizzled after her. But she,
catching the counterpane, tossed it in the air.
Down it sailed and swamped him quite.
Lightly on the window-sill she leapt,
quick –

jumped clear.

'O my poor cucumber frame!'
wailed Mother, plunging a finger in each ear.
But no crash came –
only the woodcutter's shout
as he caught her in his arms.
'Ho, ho!' Big Bear gloated. 'Two for a meal!'

Clambering on to the sill, greedily
he glowered down :
' I'll tear your bones, man, one by one ! '
But the woodcutter laughed, ' Beware my gun ! '
and cocked it. ' Insist if you wish on a guzzle,
but first, Father Bear, you must face *my* muzzle.'

' That's done it,' said Mother, and hauling him in
saw (behind the curtain)
the woodcutter laugh and lower his gun.
' The brute's off,' she said.
' Are you certain ? '
asked Father, scowling.
' Lost her, O lost her ! ' Little Bear was howling.
' Some other day,' Ma comforted, ' some other day,
my dear,' and lovingly she licked
the tears away.
But Big Bear was growling, growling
so fierce that every lark stopped singing.

Left, right ! left, right ! the woodcutter jogged
off with his gun and his merry load.
O cheerly he sang as he strode,
his rich note to the tree-tops ringing :

' Old 'oman Whiddle-Whaddle jumped out o' bed
and out o' the window she popped her head,
saying, Run, John, run, John, the grey goose is gone
and the fox is out o' the town O ! '

Heigh-ho, tick-tock,
sighed the bedroom clock.
Squeezed over the window-sill the three bears leaned
without a sound.
Heigh-ho, tick-tock.
Goodbye to the woodcutter, goodbye to Goldilocks,

goodbye (don't forget it) to the gun.
Cheerio.
Long after they'd vanished, home-faring,
the bears were at the window, spell-bound,
still staring.

THE BASILISK

(for E. B. S.)

I

In sunny Dyllos the green cabro tree frowned.
On the surprised ground a white egg
glowed, no shell to it, just a skin
and little shoulders nudged, jostled within.
It was the egg the cock laid, wrinkled to a grin.
See from the lips parted a long tongue uncurl,
flash and forward feel. On, on.
Can so much issue from so little? This long
uncoiling thing, jack-in-the-box unsprung
bewitched of motion – it is the royal train
of the basilisk. His reptilian chest
tattooed with golden chain,
in sticky dignity slow as treacle
trickles milord. 'Behold my sovran crown,
my sway tyrannical over all things
animal, human and botanical. Bow down, bow down!'
The forked tongue flickers the command.
An armadillo cracked. A cricket on a stone
threw his fiddle, ran.
And the basilisk said: 'I see it pays
to be despot of the desert ways.'

2

Noon. And the blossoms of the apricot were falling
against the desert temple, on the marble steps.
The buds of the gum tree glistened
beside the dazed rocks, the sun-giddy rocks. Listen.
A murmur from the cedar grove. The acanthus
trembled, a heron leapt
and flew, and fearfully the cactus clapped
because of the hissing and the smoke that stole

round the cedars, because of the trail of fire the basilisk blazed.
Now before the temple the stony ground reels
from his burning sceptre, his fiery policy.
Pebbles twirl and spit like catherine-wheels.
Furled in fire the hot earth aches
and subterranean Pluto quakes
as, meandering over broken places
in knotty rigmaroles and snaky mazes,
the basilisk rejoices proud as the day
along the cruel fireworks of his way.

3

Heigh slapadub over the sand Timbrello the mule
trotted with trilling of bells! on his knees
bracelets jangled, and fountain dust
sprinkled the toes of the boy astride
as he sang:

'Heigh slapadub Jolifar and
Timbrello the mule trip over the sand!
Heigh ho, isn't it grand
to be chief of a raiding robber band!'

A shadow sped over the temple track,
whipped up a finger. 'Rings on her finger!' Jolifar cried.
but the mule suddenly shied,
rose on his haunches, flung him head over heels.
Spitting sand from his mouth, rubbing it from his eyes
he stumbles to his feet. Between him and the mule he sees
lifted crest, crown of gold, the basilisk. Hush!
The neck marvellously sways as in a dream,
hoists down, shoots fierily to where
against sun-baked columns in cold
terror the mule shivers; now he draws near,
holds him in gross paralysis enchanted,
viced in torture, statue-still. Quick as murderer's knife

the forked tongue flashes at his prey
and fells him. Jolifar fled, his heels a-scare
rang grievously along the temple steps.
What did the basilisk care

as he touched the dead hoof, twined
like ivy round the forepaw and sumptuously dined?
What did he care for the boy's sorrow as
in the empty temple court satisfied
he sipped the fountain so slowly,

so steadily lifted his crown
to let the cool stream tunnel darkly down ?
And the scrounge birds settled on the carcass,
crows and kites and ravens folded their wings ;
a vulture, perched on the pastern bangle, pecked
till bangle rattled against bone.
At evening when all was finished crept
from the luckless jungle the jaguar.

4

Beside the tamarisk and the red rock
oxen turned the water-wheel, and water
spilled from clapper cups as round and round
the patient oxen trudged. And the late sun
parted the tamarisk branches, reached
for the hut, the roof of osier, touched
the stool where Nicris sat.
In a dream he saw the rock a drum
and the taut skin hummed with furies dancing, till
under the frightened patter of feet it broke
and dropped the weight – with Jolifar in his arms
he woke.
' O Nicris ! ' he sobbed, ' Nicris my father ! '
and told his gorgon tale : ' . . . cowed
I ran to the temple sanctuary, bowed
to Alaros the Snake God and spread
my offering of ainse seed, cypress and cinnamon.
But fire swallowed them ; from mating flames
three serpents swooned which with angry whip I lashed
till the great god Alaros tottered and crashed.'
So Nicris swore vengeance for the lost mule ; donned
papyrus shoes and cloak of scalps, armed himself
with spear and brass greaves that shone
bright as the Lord of Rays.
Jolifar begged him to stay, and Nicris laughed :

‘Remember how in Bactria I fought
the guardian serpents whose vermilion wings clung
to the tree of frankincense. They hung
on my neck and hid the sky from me;
and with my sword I hewed
until I killed them and in black blood rivers the life flowed
out. So——’

5

The boy clutched him, pointed over the yard where languorous
 a head
turned in the thirsty air. ‘I am ready
for battle,’ was all Nicris said.
The arched head swayed from side to side
and lazily surveyed – O basilisk, what are you dreaming,
scheming what strategy? Alert now
his gaze fixed Nicris with such torrent shock
as strikes gully, splits rock: their giant flood
staining him with murderer's blood.
Sun sparkled on his crown. Forward swept
the royal slitherslime, from yard to garden; atop the cobbled
wall straight as a string of spittle downward dribbled.
Under the tamarisk. Issuing from sun and shade,
his striped pavilion, he straightens at his victim. Enormous
sparks strike from his track. As martially he comes
silence is his music, trumpet and drums.
He calls: ‘Would you dare the marching splendour
of the noonday sun?’
The lightning leapt. And Nicris ran
for the water-trough against the wall, then faced him,
saw him pause, recoil his neck ballista-wise
poised to aim his deadly battery.
He sprang on the wooden lip, the snake after him rose
above the water – between both in the cool water
the crown sparkled. Paused on the brink to plan his way,
his eye for an instant to the mirror lowered, saw

his enemy's spear threaten from the bottom of the sky.
Up zoomed the spear ! Abrupt the image cracked,
man and sky and basilisk in splinters. The shaft shivering
pinned him to the wood, trapped. How he writhes
round its anger, with fluke and flash of tail scythes
the air ! And Nicris leapt from steam
and scalding cauldron, the drowning neck and rocket scream
of eyes ; on the safe ground watched
till stabs were faint and fainter, then
called Jolifar. Timidly they peered
among the steam (so still), drew the spear,
and the basilisk sagged to earth and lay
a mockery, a bloated, jellied thing.
Slowly like a lamp at the death of night
the eyes surrendered their light.
Doll's eyes staring from a tomb.
How dead, how strange ! Scales that stripped
the sun of burnishment divided as an earthquake
in fissures, whence the ooze of slime and green beaded foam.

6

As from madman's whip, maimed
was the evening sky. Father and son, read not
her red language, turn to the hut
and long draught of mare's milk. As hand in hand
you step lightly over the sand,
look not backwards, O read not the sky's
wounded language. High on the shelf lies
the skull flagon leather-bound,
lined in gold. Some stiffness in your arm,
some muscle torn ? Reach gently, Nicris ! In pain he rocked
against the table, limply dropped the arm that had held the spear,
the burning arm. ' My mind is clouded. I can't think.'
Easily the boy reached down the flagon, filled
it brim-full. ' Now, father, drink ! '

The half-stretched hand touched – and spilled,
suddenly crumpled as the tremor struck, as the unseen
vengeance, the living fire of the basilisk
scorched and killed.

So Nicris fell

in the dark of the tamarisk hut under
the roof of osier, charred stump of an old tree sundered.
On the earthen floor the embers crumbled
and the ash drifted up in powder, pollen air.
Blood above the hills dried to darkness.
Dark was the tamarisk hut where
spell-bound by the dead basilisk
over a black cinder the boy whimpered.

THE CAT AND THE FIDDLE

HUSH, 'tis midnight, the village slumber-bound,
ghosts and ghoulies all
fast underground :
no breath, no leaf – nor footfall, not a sound,
but –

Hey diddle diddle
the cat and the fiddle !

as up and down the kitchen floor
the tabby cat scraped a fiddler's tune –
' Head over heels and give us some more ! '
said the dog as he danced in his silver shoon
by the pearly light of the moon.
' Bravo ! ' mooed Molly the cow
from under the frosted apple bough,
and pressing her nose to the window-pane
she peeped within –
hello, on the shelf an elderly dish ;
his riveted joints were racked with pain
yet how he wished
to be able to dance again.
' Then why refrain ? '
she asked and blew him a kiss.
' Watch me ! '

Dance, dance, fiddle-dee-dee
under the cox's pippin tree !

' Bless my stumps, I can't resist ! '
said the bachelor dish,
and he put on his dancing pumps and kissed
his lover the silver spoon.
' Dear lass, we'll both be buried soon,
so dinna delay to dance with me
and dinna forget

if a jig's too ragged a step, my pet,
we can ask for a minuet.'
She helped him down to the kitchen floor,
'Try now!'
He tries.
'My poor old rickety bones!'
he cries
and groans,
'No more!'

Just then
a gust blew open the kitchen door,
the cat cried, 'Look!' and the cow cried, 'Fore!'
as away she swept with the wind galore
on high!
Think – Molly a minute ago
chewing the cud as calm as clover,
now decks awash and half-seas over
rocketing up the sky,
milk-ho! See
her fairy leap and swinging udder
(doesn't the thought of it make you shudder?),
for soon she's over the hornéd moon,
mad Molly the milker flying.
With saucy kick and flip of the heel –
the man in the moon cried, 'Imbecile!'
she sends the stars a-shying.

Hey diddle diddle
the cat and the fiddle,
the cow jumped over the moon,
and the little dog laughed to see such fun
as he danced in the light of the moon.

Meanwhile, on the kitchen shelf the plate
(or dish) antique, sedate,
who much of late

bemoaned his lonely bachelor state,
made eyes at the silver spoon.
'A boon I'd ask of you,' says he,
'my dearest love, come fly with me
to the land of the humble bumble-bee
and nuptial jollity.
If Molly the cow jumped over the moon
and knocked his loony smile awry

and kicked the stars all over the sky,
can't a bachelor dish and a spinster spoon
go honeymoon?
Hey presto, fiddle-dee-dee,
come, magic, into my wobbly knee!
The door's ajar and the garden gate,
you're seventy-seven, I'm eighty-eight –
it's not too late——'
'– none too soon,'
said the elderly spoon. 'But I like your taste.'

She kissed his shiny china face
and he tenderly clasped her slender waist
and helped her down. How grace-
fully she pirouettes ! And he ?
The moony magic anoints
his old and rickety
no longer slippery
stiff rheumaticky joints.
Away they race with quivering heart
hobbledehoy down the garden path
and out.
' Ah, bliss at last ! ' they shout.
So

Darby the dish and Joan the spoon
(the cat played the fiddle, the dog the buffoon)
eloped in the light of the moon.

Hey diddle diddle
the cat and the fiddle,
the cow jumped over the moon.
The little dog laughed to see such fun
and the dish ran away with the spoon, the spoon,
the dish ran away with the spoon.

THE BISHOP AND THE DEVIL [1]

I

UNDER the pine slopes and terraces of vine
valley-deep below a twist of sky
on the Rhone rock by the tumbling river stood his castle,
the Bishop's castle, thick-girt with ponderous walls
to keep the devil out.
Rich was his diocese, but his pride
was one tiny corner, a plot of farm 'twixt rock and river
bright with fowls marching, with the swagger
of important cloaks and legionary feathers.
Think not they were warriors these ancestors
of Chanticleer ; though dressed in military satins,
their lists were the choir stalls at matins
where wild of temperament they tourneyed
and tossed the song hits from the psalms.
The Bishop treated them as sons and daughters,
so loving them he built their quarters
as splendid as his castle. A Persian carpenter
made furniture of cedarwood, perches
of slender silver birch, while a master
potter from Pekin moulded beds of alabaster.
Plumed in black and gold with scarlet comb
and feathers streaming lustrous, the cock Fortissimo
was lord of this domain. He was the tenor solo –
his highest note full throttle
had been preserved in spirits in a bottle.
Stretched upon his toes, with neck as long
as a chameleon's tongue he sang and trumpeted
above the clucking chorus.
The kindly Bishop proud of their display
fed his singing birds on curds and whey
and had the muckyard perfumed twice a day.

[1] Theodule was the first Bishop of Sion in the Rhone Valley, A.D. 381–391. The high Alpine pass joining Zermatt with the plains of Italy was named after him.

2

These were his merriment, his sorrow's antidote.
When they sang not his soul was troubled and his chest
heaved on grievous billows of unrest.
Unknown and friendless he was, his fame
empty as his church for few knew his name.
Among the scattered valleys, from Prato to the vineyards
of Finellen, he had carefully presented
each chalet with hymnal and psalter, but as clocks
weren't invented and the church had no chime
no one went to worship for no one knew the time.
What use were clever sermons, a church
paved with papal wealth,
when the sum congregation was the barnyard and himself?
Years passed in prayerful sorrow and unfriended desolation.
Though mocked by the devil he never gave up hope—
and one day decided, 'I'll go and see the Pope.'
But the devil, arch-fiend and eavesdropper, overheard
by the tell-tale window the Bishop's words
and rejoiced mightily. 'Here's a chance
to bag a soul,' he said, and followed Stygian-dressed,
decked out in verdigris and all his blackest best.

3

After the avalanche of wind,
after the laboured climbing, the frozen breathing, at last
loosed from the mountain's grip what bitterness to find—
three days, a hundred leagues from home—Lombardy lost
in snow, fields fast in winter's clutch, and Rome
fingered with icicles and tentacled with frost.
The Bishop's teeth chattered as wrapped
in bishop's woollies over the frozen Tiber over the snows
of the seven hills he goes.
Head-high under the moon he marched, the stars
his guide, Orion and Osiris and the Twins.

' It's cold,' said Aquarius the water-carrier.
' All my pipes are frozen.' ' In this bitter weather,'
said the Plough, ' the ground's hard as flint
and my share 's blunt.'
Outside the Pope's palace under the Pole star
where the papal torch flowered from the chapel ridge
and down-street the sparks showered, here
poor men fiddled and danced
by braziers under the warmth of the moon.
The devil unseen unchariotted
swept up and circled overhead.
' I'm shivering, I must hurry,' said the Bishop,
chilled to the bone.
As he reached the ante-chapel, with a snap the roof-rail bust
and all the snow dropped like a noisy ghost
plop beside him, missed him just.
Under the cross the torch hissed,
flickered and fizzled out.
' The devil's riding the roofs tonight,' said the Bishop
and ran for the papal chamber.

4

O treasury of riches, warmth and beauty multiform!
Out of the cruel night his fingers glowed;
how fast his heart beat
as he knelt subservient at his Holiness' feet!
At last he raised his eyes, all wonder
at the hall flaked with dragon scales,
the ivory pillars and jewelled tables,
mysterious tapestries, walls that masters of astronomy
had pictured with the universe by Ptolemy—
planetary signs, crescents, zodiacs,
the dotted galaxy, sun and moon
and many astronomical knick-knacks.
' O let me not swoon,' murmured the Bishop,
' let me not swoon!'

5

With marble countenance the Pope heard his tale
of church empty, of doors flung wide
to men who never came.
Then casually, but impassive still,
'Do you like music?' he asked. 'Are you musical?'
That started the Bishop off. 'If I had my choir-birds here,
the black and gold cock (Fortissimo's his name)——'
but the Pope clapped for silence, and
suddenly out of the darkness conjured such a sound
as jumbled light and shadow, jangled the chandeliers
and made the Bishop's toes tingle. 'Don't
be scared,' said the Pope and ghost-gliding on the vibrant floor
parted the curtains over the chapel door,
disclosing, while the room throbbed still,
monstrous in the dimness – a bell.
'I present you with Time,' he said,
'a full congregation and blessings on your head.
In Sion tower
sound the matins hour!
it shall be heard from Prato to the vineyards of Finellen,
from Visp to Lake Lemanus where before the wind
on wings of red the busy traders run.
A monster bell indeed! It weighs a ton
and rings loud enough to rouse the midnight sun.'

6

In the street of the popinjays the poor men danced
and a fiddle scraped the boots along, while overhead
heigh-ho the devil pranced on his hobby-horse the air.
The palace door banged. 'Now's my chance!' the devil said.
Down he swept straight at the Bishop's soul
as it trundled down the steps.
'Pardon me!' he coughed. 'Isn't there
a snag? Carry a ton over the Alps –

how's that to be done ? '
The Bishop stopped. He knew the voice, a familiar one,
frankly admitted he hadn't thought of that.
' Perhaps I could help you ? What about a chat
by the brazier ? ' the devil said.
(The poor men dropped their dance and fled.)
' I'm quite prepared to carry the bell
and, if you like, yourself as well
quick as a flash to Sion castle.'
' By dawn tomorrow ? '
' Before dawn, I promise.'
' And your terms?'
' Strictly cash.
Tomorrow you must give me your soul,
pledge me stoutly to abjure the Trinity
and pray devoutly to the Prince of hell.
In your heart's blood sign my scroll
and all you want shall be yours, the mysteries
of heaven and earth, Helen of Troy's lips
and the usual rigmarole.'
He smiled and stretched red fingers to the glow
while red coals spilt blood upon the snow.
Continuing :
' Lovely it is to kill and not suffer as a murderer,
to steal and not suffer as a thief,
never to doubt or fear the consequence.
Blessed are the murderers, the thieves, the embezzlers,
the forgers, the drunkards, the hired assassins——'
But the Bishop heard nothing. He was thinking
of home ; warm in his imagining saw
himself in the barnyard, fowls following
greedy for crumbs from his apron, Fortissimo holloing,
' Stop, master ! hear how I sing ! ' —
himself fastened in the enchanted ring.
Then a voice crept into his dream
and whispered, ' Dawn's your watchword ! The devil

promised for dawn ! Listen, here's a trick
to sell your soul and keep your bishopric ! ' . . .
' Deception's a sin,' thought the Bishop, ' but I shan't suffer,'
and he promptly accepted the devil's offer.

7

Snug in the devil's pack he watched
the Eternal City vanish, Arno, the Tuscan Apennines,
and plains of Lombardy. Fast they journeyed
with enormous stride as the giant waterfall,
the long leaper. And always the bell,
strung by halter to the devil's back,
behind them carved out a moonlit track.
As they mounted the horizon sank
and rim on rim the hills fell away to the utter dark.
Through the slender forests where the air bit keen,
over trees they passed that deep in the snow
dreamed the winter through,
beyond the highest pines, lone stragglers,
out in a minute on to the mountain edge
(one larch clings to the crumbling ledge),
by cornices where ice strings hung
perilous and beautiful, firm against a wind
that pawed, thrust, tore, no gentleness in it.
And above them rose the white peaks, remote and shining.
At the top of the pass the devil tripped,
jarred the Bishop such a jolt
that he fell like a thunderbolt,
jogged and bumped down the glacier course till the fiend
fleet-following (the poor bell gonging
from boulder ice to boulder)
caught him and hoisted him bruised
on to his shoulder.
At last in the swallowed gloom far far under
a moonbeam touched the castle rock, conjured his home

from the sleeping valley. 'Faster!' said the devil, 'Faster!' –
the rims of the hills were beginning to shine.
With chamois feet down he flashed
past Prato and St. Nicholas,

8

to the first field of Sion and the noisy river,
hurtled over the bridge and through
the misty pines till the castle came in view.
'Prepare to sign your soul away!' he chortled,
and running rattled the scroll.
'You forget,' replied
the Bishop, 'I've still a hundred yards to ride.'
The devil laughed. 'Have you power to pull
the bedclothes off the sleeping sun
before my hundred yards is run?'
For answer out of the sack the Bishop leapt
and in a loud voice cried:
'Coq, chante!
Que tu chantes!
Ou que jamais plus tu ne chantes!'
A shadow grew out of the wall as he spoke
and towered against the blue. Stretched on his toes
behold Fortissimo – he crows! 'Welcome! greeting
to my master! greeting to the dawn!' The night breaks
and straight the chinks of day stretch and strain
the sky. A pace from the castle wall the devil stops.
The race lost, he drops the bell amazed.
'Chase him!' cried the Bishop. 'Chase him!'
Down jumped the cock. The shady battlement
crumbled into feather flakes as
with whirring wings the fowls went chasing after.
The devil turned and with strangled oaths leapt
over the snow gymnastical, all angles in the air.
Close at heel the cock launched out like a battering-ram

and the whole barnyard charged after,
swooping, tumbling, tripping, flapping,
squawking, creaking, scraping, clapping.
Snow flung from their feet flew wide
and the hills in pale confusion fled.
Alone, the Bishop sank to his knee.
'O God omnipotent,' he said,
'I yield the world to Thee.'

9

Now rivals, bell and choir contend
for their master's highest pleasure. When
the bell hurls his thunderbolt of sound
the villages are emptied all around
and throng to hear the clucking canticles. Then –
if the jealous choir condescend –
both voices blend.
The service over, 'Master,' they urge,
'We have done our best.
Which of us makes you happier ?' And hard pressed
the Bishop answers, 'Neither, my dears. I count myself
twice blest.'

THE LAY OF URASHIMA

I

SHUT out the night, draw close
to the fire and listen. This is the tale of Urashima
the fisher lad, of the seventh generation
of seafarers, humble folk that het or wet
blow or snow combed the deep for its yield –
red breme, flounder, sole, the whetstone
cuttlefish, whatever might fetch a dime or two
or grace some wealthy dish. *By toil and moil*
we work the sea, waist-deep in the slippery smell
of cod and hake and mackerel
as we bob on the bustuous wave, fearless
for all his lion roar. Meanwhile high overhead
the clouds, lazy voyagers, crowd canvas and
with no wave-slap, no creak of tackle, sail
effortless their rich armada across heaven.
We envy their quiet sea. . . .
But my story. . . .
'Twas the month of icicles, snow-deep December ;
over all had winter spread his white mantle
and left bare only the sea, the raw whipped-bitter wave.
A day for chimneys and the flying spark. (More
coal, son. Draw closer, hands to the blaze.)
Was Urashima by his chimney ? Not he,
but away out fishing for a wager, this fool
in derring-do. ' It's perishy cold and I'm clammed,'
says he. ' Not even a tiddler's bite for me,'
when lo the line drags heavy, slow ;
some monster must be. What prow-face this
holes the wave, drawn hard, reluctantly ?
A tortoise, in such
chill sea ! He draws her to him (piteous
beseeching eyes), strokes the underchin,
rough wrinkles, with his blue

fingers : 'Tortoise steak ? Too tough –
who wants the belly ache ?' – and throwing her back
he rebaits the hook and waits . . .

and waits

till over the wave a strange voice
hailed him, haunting low, sweet
as honeysuckle : 'Urashima ! Urashima !'
Straight below him the brave tortoise
full-faced him on a hillock wave and
quite fluently addressed him thus :
'Dear sir, thank you for your favour. 'Tis
blindness of men to kill heedlessly, at will ;
seldom is such kindness as this
that I have savoured. O kindest, from my heart
I pray you journey with me to the joyous isle
of Rin Jin, the Sea King. 'Tis an only land
where time basks a hundred years in one
mortal day, where the seasons in fourfold
pageantry link and hand in hand
on mountain, furrow, holt and silver sand
tread their stately saraband.
O kindest, come with me to the island oversea.
R.S.V.P.'

The lad leapt. 'O yes,' he cried ;
but weighed a little sadly : 'I have a home
and family,' mused awhile. Then
with a flash of fire, 'Yet I'm young,
unwed, and would be full and free.
I'll come, gladly.'

2

He mounted. Spreadeagle on the wave the tortoise
like a speedboat smacked the waters, sped
over ocean, trailing white miles of sea.
O she raced the lightning (slow as the hare,
the saying goes, swift as the whirlwind tortoise

and the windy snail) and the foam flying head-high
at the lad splashed him yet soaked him no whit,
nor was he chill at all, but each moment warm
and warmer still.

So to the island. No wildings grow. On trees
set in leaves of lapis lazuli
rubies glow. D'you hear the throstle ? and
the spink ? the bangle song of rills that flash
white fingers down the hills ? the gonging
of falls from headland to the sea ? Deep
in the water coralline, fish long-robed and wavy
splash and sing and play. 'Tis an only land
where time basks a hundred years in one
mortal day, where the seasons in fourfold
pageantry link and hand in hand
on mountain, furrow, holt and silver sand
tread their stately saraband.
The tortoise
was fled. Hard by a seahorse was gambolling
and prancing. His rein trailed in the sea, he champed
at the bit, his teeth clucked like castanets.
' O ride me, knight-at-arms, ride me. I'll rock you
home to Rin Jin's daughter, Princess
of the Sea.' Pygmy charger, frail yet
mettlesome, how you cleave the wave asunder !
Away rode Urashima to more wonder.

3

Maiden on the sand lay,
on the sand summer's child
Liasne ; she was ageless, with eyes
of blossom and foliage of hair
wind-wild.

Well was her beauty,
each moment new-born ;
fine as wings of dragonfly
from chrysalis flown
this morn.

Well was the melody
of her maiden voice,
gentle as footfall, as
footfall in the Garden
of Paradise.

Well was her figure –
how high ? Were she a bride,
then high as a man's heart. 'Mine,'
said Urashima, 'my heart ! '
he cried.

4

I'll not waste to say what miracle he felt
as now with leaping heart he woke to manhood.
He knelt to beauty new and strange,
his first of love.

'Do you remember me,
Urashima ? '

He shook his head.

'I was
the tortoise,' she smiling said. 'So disguised
I tried you and found you kindest of men.'

He laughed loud. 'Why, but for a wager——' he began,
but wiser held his tongue.

'The heart
that threw me to the tide wins me, if he will,
for bride.'

She clapped her·hands. Through the flowered
sea, the jungle coralline, lo
a great company of fishes floating
brought her wedding robe, spangled, ceremonious,
of fire and gold, all colours of the sun-steeped
wave. (Can a maid forget her ornament,
a bride her attire ?) Others bore in fins
trays piled with frumenty, sops-in-wine
and wedding cup.
And as they drank and ate
and watched, all wonder, dolphins played soft music
(bubbles flying from instruments like
whirling horses at a fair). Some
blew oboes, not a few
stepped a strange measure on the white sand.
Then the angel sang (with wings for fins
and halo), rolled her fat voice sonorously forth ;
the porpoise danced a minuet ; the whale –
well, no tongue can tell how heartily
he made the ocean swell ; till last,
mumbudgeting along in the after-lull
Old King Cole the merry old Sole puffed
with his train of tiddlers three. O there was delight
in isle and the salt sea
for man, bird, beast, fish, herb and green tree.

5

'Come follow,' she bade him, and from a headland,
tower of four suns, showed him the seasons
side by side : autumn folk that frisked home-along
by nearly naked boughs ; iced winter,
cattle plodding with slow thighs over the snow ;
spring matted with primrose and wild hyacinth,
the wind brisk as pony trot ; and summer,
thyme-and-bracken-sweet – see the fork-wing bird

fly, how low ! – ah summer,
and the warm dark secret woods of summer.
They lay there, in those woods.

Long they dallied
in pleasaunce of love, as in a cave far
indrawn where no sea laps, tempest-lorn,
no ripple breaking. 'Out, let the hoarse wind
howsoever shout and hallo ! I'll
go no more a-roving,' said Urashima.
'Let there be no waking.' And his wild spirit,
in passion's afteryield of quiet
(lagoon-still, of the deepest flower of the sea,
sangrail of love), rests. 'I'll go no more
a-roving.' So, beyond time they lay,
drowned in sweeter than sleep, far ocean down,
lullay, where tranquillest,
till – a rippling :
Tippiwit ! pire-eek . . . ki-ki-ki . . . lovers, wake !
He slept still, but she
raised her dreaming lashes. 'Listen, the lark
of morning,' she murmured. *Lovers, wake !*
Come hither ! come hither ! come hither !

6

On the fourth day as they sat by the shore the wind
spoke to Urashima : 'Come with me, son,
from this strange isle come home with me. I bowl
winter back and oversea unroll
the spring' : temptingly, 'I bring fair
wave-weather to your land. See the harbour bud
unfold as the fleet moves, outspreading. O blossom,
O sun-red sails !'

'I remember,' sighed
Urashima, 'swing of the rocking wave
my life, sea toil that was my duty, danger
and delight. . . . But I'll not go back.'
Then the wind breathed
home and wept his mother's tears: 'Where are you, my son?
Like the wild swan flown so madly?
or drowned? Come back to me, my son.'
Liasne
frowned. 'What moves him to look so sadly? hour after hour
to moon like a pot-sick window-flower?'
'Let me go,'
he said suddenly, 'for one day, one hug
of home. Give me the fastest tortoise, I'll
be back in a day, I promise.'
'O stay,'
she begged, 'lest our love falter and fall and lose
her song.'
'Can a man for ever sprawl in a nest
and lisp of love?'
'Wretched prisoner,' she scoffed,
'condemned to drag the stones of love along!'

He bit his anger, spoke gently till
she softened and let him go. And she gave him
for surety of their love a parting gift,
box of the jewel hand. 'Hold it close,'
she told him tearfully. 'It shall keep you
safe.' And as he kissed her she added fearfully,
'Beware never to open it.'
'I'll never open it,'
he said.
And the tortoise, the ocean-thrasher,
brought him to his own country.

7

He leapt to shore and ran to harbour, singing :
By toil and moil
we work the sea, waist-deep in the slippery smell
of cod and hake and mackerel
as we bob on the bustuous wave. . . .
But where are the ships,
the sea that tumbled ? Sand is the sea now,
the ships are buried, stone has crumbled. See
the clouds sail overhead, lone voyagers.
'Is my mother well ? my father well ? I must
to the harbour hill, the house by the juniper,
my home. . . .' There's no tree now, and what's
this mort of rubble and weed and bone ?
'Four days ago we flourished in this land,'
he wept in anger.
A thin wind stirred over the sand
as the voice of the dead wailed answer : 'Our dust has lain
for centuries. We don't know you. Who are you,
stranger ?'
'I am Urashima. I sailed
four days ago.'
'So recently ? You sailed
four centuries ago,' they wailed, 'poor ghost !'
and pitied him. And the wind faded from
that waste of rubble and weed and bone.

8

And Urashima stared at the wave that rolled him
from that far isle over sunken
centuries to this aged shore.
'Sun-shower and Liasne, I had two blessings
in one ; now so poor am I, none—yet how rich
when I sat in her shadow and never missed

the sun ! ' He called her name and clapped
for the tortoise three times –
no tortoise came, none came to him as he watched
alone in that melancholy sand between
printless dune and sad sombre wave slow unfurling ;
wide, infinitely sad. ' Ah foam-flower,
narcissus of the wave, nodding
white fields, I'd gather you all, heap
high for Liasne – if I could ride home to her,
if I could ride.'

After long waiting he remembered
her gift, the box of the jewel hand. ' Dare I untie
the silken thread and open it ? As surety
of our love it may show me a way . . . better risk that
than stay.' With trembling fingers he
slid off the lid. A white cloud
rushed out sighing, hovered a moment
in the sky and swept out to sea. The box
broke in his hand. ' My promise ! ' he cried,
and grew wondrous weary. Four hundred years
bowed him to the ground, bloated his fingers to
an old man's, of gnarled olive – *how tender and slender*
were her hands ! – hooped his back so he hobbled with spine
of waggon wheel. *How did she move ?*
Easy in gliding motion, light
as a water-skate she skimmed the iceless wave.
His white hair blew in the wind. His face
with runlet tears was a rain-worn stone.
Can hers be too ? . . . Gods, lest that be so
roll back your world to yesterday !

He fell.

Sand pillowed his head and the cold
tide, stealing the last warmth of his lips,
wound him in her shroud.

9

Would you know more (said the story-teller), unlock the door
of an old man of memory ? I was wrecked
on the Isle of Rin Jin, on the silver sand danced
with the seasons their saraband, and from the tower
of four suns myself saw Liasne. Her eyes
were dim, sloe-lustreless ; she wandered
from season to season, crouching by winter (fire
had cold lips), catching spring by the hand
(how frosty her fingertips !), lying in the lap
of summer (O thyme-and-bracken-sweet, and the fork-wing bird
low flying !) but the summer wind
breathed on her cheek ice. Pity
the doom in her heart, and none to share
the dreadful dwelling there. . . .

Does she still wander ?

No (said the story-teller). She broke the storm grip ;
the flower, freed, leapt from her heart ;
he grows there, Urashima, seed of the vast
troubled waters, strong, exquisite. He is
so passing merry (she said), his laugh
like a drumming of drums, while his least smile
would start a shock of dolphins from the grey-faced sea.
Can these things be ?

I have your answer
(said the story-teller). I found it in the harbour sand,
this, the box of the jewel hand, the broken pieces
self-mended. And here, where I cleaned what rust
had bitten, see in plain words
my story written.

Sonnets

NORTH WALES

TODAY the mountain closes in coldness,
climber leans for shelter and no birds pass ;
obscurely cloud smoulders as the trail
that sun fires burnt in summer grass.
Now grows the storm ; gorse crouches, pointing
frightened fingers from old hands ;
and pygmy bracken, eyes to the height, mocks
the exposed dangerous anatomy of trees.
Chained to the gale they strain,
snap and scatter limbs down granite rock.
But stoop to earth and hear how the wind
that paced the enormous hill-top and hurled
war at the ragged wood is only
a whisper to the wise ground-clutching world.

THE CLIMBERS

WILD shadows take the summit at a stride.
Not these who, as covetous, scratch hours
on the crag, whose loss to the indifferent
mountain is less than a stone. See closer how
as spiders they enmesh the rock from boss
to chockstone and by traverse to
the odd sudden pinnacle ; not clinging
as spiders, trust to a clinker.
Complete they straddle the ridge now, where eye
ropes them to snow and far shine of sea ;
then drop for shelter to the shoulder and reclined
in heather sense sun's thrill on numb fingers
and down gullies of choked minds
the coursing waters and white sound of the sea.

SPRING IN THE MOUNTAINS

So April, and all the sky is water ; ice
crashes, rattle the screes on Tryfan ; the rill
in the gully marsh, trailing Ophelia tresses,
soaks and sluggish lies. Each hour on the hill
a lamb is born, while by wet sides
of peat and wasted heather root (pale
as clean skeletons, late the sirens' prey),
waiting his moment a fox lurks to kill.
And the clouds that pace restless over Llewelyn,
for ever racing but for ever still
like runners painted on a vase, shall hold
their strange stationary course until,
time and the mountains melting, they from the sun
drop to the level world and freely run.

THE FOX

FIRST lambs have come, late snowfall to the hill.
All day he watches, feeding on greed
till, stars in the April sky, he steals
shadows down the valleyside, furtive wades
marsh myrtle and by screen of heather comes
where flocks graze. Trembling for quarry
he scans each plucking lamb, chooses, pauses
strong as a spell, then flashes to revelry.

The lambless ewe sputters down the slope.
Home over Bristling Ridge in one sweep
he covers the Glyders, then deviously to his deep
mountain den, safe down creviced drop
where no terrier dares.
On his morning round
death in wool embers is the shepherd's find.

WILD MOUNTAINS AND A VALLEY STREWN WITH ROCKS

As the clean wall that cloud builds
screening hill and wiping all feature,
as new marble no sculptor yet moulds,
so smooth once was the face of this mountain :
till storm playing for fancy chiselled realms
of royalty and with abrasion rounded
bastion and dome celestial, or hollowed
dungeons where weather drips on fallen kings.

Aeolus, keeper of winds, who loosed them on
this mountain, be thanked for the shock volted with
thunder,
the clumsy gift of tumbled splendour,
grey pearls in the valley, stones
unstrung from high necklaces, shale, frozen boulders,
and what the torrent flings, – all your plunder.

EARLY WINTER ON A FARM NEAR BAIAE

(After Martial)

So crammed the corn tumbles from chink and crevice,
jars steam the odour of old wine.
Now is November : running from winter
all haste the farmer steals the last grape. Down-valley
the bass echo of bull lowing, where his calf
on baby legs swaggers for fight.
Fowl tread the muckyard,
Speckled guinea-hens, flamingos winged with fire,
pheasants flown from lands of sorcery.
A squawking gander splashes gems the peacock wears.

Listen ! the woodbird calls, now the dove,
and towers ring to feather sounds. Suddenly
spying the farmwife, hogs with greedy gallop snort
to her apron. One lamb lonely, mother-longing,
bleats for her, peeps ever to her pasture.

THE BARGE

WILD blackberry tangles the bank ; the dusty
towpath trails to water that reflects a verge
of trees, cool philosophers, divers for rusty
treasures of deep learning. Now a barge
disturbs them on their strip of ocean,
slow heavy-gliding with full hidden hold,
dirty as smoke, beautiful in motion
as smoke drifting over furrowed field.

Patient, flurried for nobody's sake,
the barge wears a day into a week ;
it does not impress the water ; one white
tiny blossom alone flatters its wake,
trying (minnow and whale) to imitate
the majestically proud coal-shoddy ship of state.

SLEEP

FROM the slow solemn ticking on the stair,
from cheek fast in pillow and chin
in eiderdown, from limbs yet sensate,
to the breathing of a new nerveless air.
My heart is not mine now nor yours,
for Life holds it close in his hand ;
he is the pilot of my nightly ship
and Love the moving sea between the shores.
But O the anguish and the death when
the day raider comes and at a bound
destroys our quiet harbour ! Ear listens
to what fingers feel – the cruelty and burning.
the noisy stolen tide, and eye
sees anchor broken and the dear sea dry.

Miscellaneous

ST. BRENDAN AND THE FISHES

1

St. Brendan chanted mass in voyage
over the sabbath-quiet sea,
and seven frail land-longing brothers
    listened fearfully.

' Master, sing lower ! Monsters
under our keel fiercely fly.
If you anger them with chanting, we
    must surely die.'

St. Brendan laughed loud : ' O Lord,
have pity on Thy wayward sheep ! '
In answer four creatures zoomed
    up from the deep –

    Agg the sea-cat, inveterate in wiles,
    Puff the Angel, like a pillow,
    Old Whacker the whale and
    Moon-splinter, minnow.

2

On wobble knees the brothers watched
four perils nibble at the rudder.
' Lord Jesus, hinder these fish or find them
    other fodder ! '

But they for joy of Paul's Feast
made merry with water sport
and fun frolic, doing the voyagers
no hurt,

till, high song over, St. Brendan
said, 'Fish, that's all for today.'
In wave-scrubble tails wiggle and fluke,
flick and away –

Agg the sea-cat, inveterate in wiles,
Puff the Angel, like a pillow,
Old Whacker the whale and
Moon-splinter, minnow.

THE HEN AND THE CARP

ONCE, in a roostery,
there lived a speckled hen, and when-
ever she laid an egg this hen
ecstatically cried :
' O progeny miraculous, particular spectaculous,
what a wonderful hen am I ! '

Down in a pond near by
perchance a gross and broody carp
was basking, but her ears were sharp –
she heard Dame Cackle cry :
' O progeny miraculous, particular spectaculous,
what a wonderful hen am I ! '

' Ah, Cackle,' bubbled she,
' for your single egg, O silly one,
I lay at least a million ;
suppose for each I cried :
" O progeny miraculous, particular spectaculous ! "
what a hullaballoo there'd be ! '

THE MARCH PAST

As I sit in a ditch musing, enjoying
this windy morning, the trees doing a roaring
trade in clap and chatter, the green world
about my head in turmoil, sorrel and foxtail
bur-marigold minute gentianella
shouting their heads off, – as I sit here musing,

suddenly HONK ! a horn. On the ribbon road
over switchback of hillocks comes primly a procession
of khaki buggies. The first passes me, ' caution
left-hand drive ', next and next, hundreds of 'em
precisely the same, speckless, exact as
clockwork ; in each a khaki driver and four seats
empty (what waste of space for lasses).
So Canada comes. We cheer, wave you
green hands, all flora's wildness.
Meanwhile,

beyond where the swallows dip, in lavish
pantomime heaven apes this prim procession,
monstrously – great clumsy chariots of clouds
with smoky misfit wheels ; woolly warriors
reclining on cushions that stick out
everywhere. How flopping unhurriedly they jog
to what odd battle ! Alone one martial figure,
the Gallant Sun, all his medals shining,
stands for Salute.

THE SQUIRREL

AMONG the fox-red fallen leaves I surprised him. Snap
up the chestnut bole he leapt,
the brown leaper, clawing up-swept :
turned on the first bough and scolded me roundly.
That's right, load me with reviling,
spit at me, swear horrible, shame me if you can.
But scared of my smiling
off and up he scurries. Now Jack's up the beanstalk
among the dizzy giants. He skips
along the highest branches, along
tree-fingers slender as string,
fur tail following, to the very tips :
then leaps the aisle –
O fear he fall
a hundred times his little length !
He's over ! clings, swings on a spray,
then lightly, the ghost of a mouse, against the sky traces
for me his runway of rare wonder, races
helter-skelter without pause or break
(I think of the snail – how long would he take ?)
on and onward, not done yet –
his errand ? some nut-plunder, you bet.
Oh he's gone !
I peer and search and strain for him, but he's gone.
I wait and watch at the giants' feet, among
the fox-red fallen leaves. One drop
of rain lands with a smart tap
on the drum, on parchment leaf. I wait
and wait and shiver and forget. . . .
A fancy : suppose these trees, so ancient, so
venerable, so rock-rooted, suddenly

heaved up their huge elephantine hooves
(O the leaves, how they'd splutter and splash
like a waterfall, a red waterfall) – suppose
they trudged away !
What would the squirrel say ?

THE OLD ELM TREE

A DAY heavy with summer and the lilac's scent
I passed you where you stood
by a droughty rutted lane behind the wood,
old, a little bent
under your weight of finery, somehow familiar.
I was a stranger but I could swear
I'd seen you before.

I know. You're a granny, wrinkled, and you've lost
your figure : not like the airling willow,
minionette, self-gazer in the mirror shallows.
I saw you once at midsummer market enquiring the cost
of onions ; you were parcelled in yards of summer cotton –
a garden and crescent moon the pattern ;
something amused you and with a lift
of ' good gracious ' hands, a shake
of frumpery, you began to quab and quake,
spill in ripples of excessive laughter ;
then some weeks after
I saw you at the street corner waiting for the bus –
plenty of time, my dear, it was silly
to have hurried – and as it rumbled up the rise,
all anxiety your pointing brolly
agitated to poke out the driver's eyes.

A BIRD PAINTED ON THE SEVENTH PAGE OF A MEDIEVAL PSALTER

DELIGHTED by this quaint illumination the eye traces
lilies set in emerald emblazonry,
and grasses – a wiregold filigree
no weed or nettles tangle.
Much metallic here, all would jangle in a breeze.

Bird, flier above, how's your living? where your hunting bent?
I see insects among these frail paradisal daisies,
and below in this alphabet inscribed in praises
your nourishment.
Or do you always ride rushing high,
the bright beak up-pointed
as if to spit a thunderbolt?

The beak is perilous, the vivid eyes revolt,
yet wings are restful – curious disjointed
picture. May nothing fret those wings,
the vaulted tracery arched above centuries
of air. Trees – pillars to leaf clerestories,
to heaven's roof in miniature –
are climbing like questions to you where, not recognised, not
heard,
yourself a secret you span an unknown heritage.

Brighter than pigment, old as parchment page,
who, what are you, secret Delphian bird?

M. K. S.

TODAY I walk in the woods where last year
I wheeled you. In this half-light and alone
I am plunged in the cool sunk world of Oceanus where
leaf and brake are bright scales and highest branches the moan
of far reefers. Now from slipping shade
the beeches flower and lacquered weed
floats in slow symphonies. A diver's line below the light
of birds and lanced foam, dark sea-swallowed am I.
Sudden grief makes me unmanly as I see
your eyes, and my head swims in memory of those eyes stored
with icebergs ; for these were pain – a white
fraction visible, a whole sum unseen – no suns ever thawed.

And I remember death's glad instant, the morning
when cruelty crumbled. Then must the ice have crumbled and
Atlantic birds
sheered in dismay from spilling crystals. Did the iron gloves of
Thor
clap thunder oversea ? or was death no roar,
only a quiet quick melting as if tropic suns were burning
winter in Labrador ?

Printed in Great Britain by R. & R. CLARK, LIMITED, *Edinburgh*